The Pride Street Crew

7

Say It To My Face

Mike Wilson

Published in association with
The Basic Skills Agency

Hodder & Stoughton

A MEMBER OF THE HODDER

Acknowledgements
Cover: Jim Eldridge
Illustrations: Jim Eldridge

Orders; please contact Bookpoint Ltd, 39 Milton Park, Abingdon, Oxon OX14 4TD. Telephone: (44) 01235 400414, Fax: (44) 01235 400454. Lines are open from 9.00–6.00, Monday to Saturday, with a 24 hour message answering service. Email address: orders@bookpoint.co.uk

British Library Cataloguing in Publication Data
A catalogue record for this title is available from the British Library

ISBN 0 340 77636 6

First published 2000
Impression number 10 9 8 7 6 5 4 3 2 1
Year   2005 2004 2003 2002 2001 2000

Typeset by GreenGate Publishing Services, Tonbridge, Kent.
Printed in Great Britain for Hodder and Stoughton Educational, a division of Hodder Headline Plc, 338 Euston Road, London NW1 3BH, by Atheneum Press, Gateshead, Tyne & Wear

JOHN / BONE

WESLEY / TALL

LUKE / SKY

SIMON / CUSTARD

CARL / SPOT

Mark Paine came up behind me,
and smacked me on the back of the head.
It hurt, but I didn't let him see that.

'What have you been saying about me?'
he asked.

'Oh. Hi, Mark,' I said,
as cool as I could.
'What's up?'

'You've been saying things
behind my back,' he said.

'What things?' I asked.

Mark Paine jabbed a finger at my face.

'You can say it to my face,' he said.
'Or don't say it at all.
Keep it to yourself.
OK?'

'I don't know what you're talking about …'

But Mark Paine had gone.

I was coming out of school
with Bone.
There were some girls there.
They all went very quiet.

'What was that all about?' Bone asked.

'Don't know,' I said.

'What have you been saying about him?'

'Nothing!' I said.
'He's just making it up.'

'What for?'

'Don't know,' I said again.

Mark Paine was in our year.

He lived on Power Street,
one road down from Pride Street.
But we didn't know him very well.

He kept himself to himself.

He came to our school in Year Nine.
At first, he was always in fights.
Then he seemed to settle down a bit.

We forgot about him.

Mark Paine was big.

Bone told me he did boxing
on Friday nights
down at the Youth Club.

'What are you going to do?' asked Bone.

'Nothing,' I said.
'It's just a mistake.
He must be mixing me up
with someone else.'

'I can find out who is really to blame,'
I went on.

'Then it won't be me that gets it.
It will be someone else!'

I was thinking back
to a fight Mark had,
when he first came to school.

I can still see the blood
fall from Wayne Taylor's mouth.
I can still see his broken tooth
skid across the floor of the classroom ...

Next day,
Mark came up to me again.
I was waiting with some other kids
to go in to Winker Watson's maths class

He said to me,
'You just don't listen, do you?'

'Mark,' I said,
'it's a mistake ...'

'*You* made the mistake,' he said.
'I've heard the lies you've told.
I know what you're up to.'

Everyone was looking at us.
Mark reached over and grabbed my hand.
I tried to pull away,
but he was too strong.

He held my arm under his arm.
He held my fingers in his fist.
He was going to crunch them down
until they went crack.

'It's going to stop,' he went on.
'Right now. Or else …'

Crunch.

It didn't really hurt.
My fingers just went sort of numb.
Nothing was broken.

But this had to stop.
He was getting to me.
I had to do something.

I asked everyone,
What's up with Mark Paine?
Why has he got it in for me?
Who is saying things about him
and what are they saying?

I asked Carl.
He said, 'He's just stupid.
He had it in for me
some time last year.
Until he went off the idea.'

'He kept calling me a snob.
I didn't even know what a snob was.
I had to go and look it up.'

'What shall I do?' I asked.

'Stand up to him,' said Carl.
'That's my advice.'

'But he'll kill me!' I said.

'That's a chance you'll have to take,' he said.

'Well … what did *you* do?' I asked.
'When he was after you
did *you* stand and fight?'

'No way,' he said.
'I kept out of his way.
What do you think I am, stupid?'

That night, I did the right thing.
I stayed behind at school.
I had asked to see Miss Green.
I was going to tell her about Mark Paine.

I went to her office and waited.
I could hear Miss Green inside,
talking to someone. A woman.

I waited.

That's how come I was there
when Miss Green came out.
A woman with dark hair came out with her.
After her came Mark Paine.

Miss Green was saying,
'Thank you ever so much, Mrs Paine.
Thank you for letting us know ...
We'll keep an eye on him for you
and we'll watch Mark's grades this term ...

'And, Mrs Paine,
if there's anything we can do to help ...
anything at all ...'

Mark saw me.
So he knew that I knew.

He looked down.
I looked down.

I watched,
as he went with his Mum
out to the car park.

Miss Green turned to me.

'Now then, young man,' she said.
'You wanted to see me ...'

'No, miss,' I said.
'I think I'm all right now.'

A few days later, at home.

I was waiting for a phone call from Lizzy.
We were going to go to the cinema.
My Mum was on the phone.
I was hanging round her,
trying to get her to hurry up.

I wasn't listening on purpose.
I wasn't being nosy
but I did hear what she was saying.

'Really?' she said.
'How old is she ...
the same old story ...'

'So – did he meet her at work, then?
They always meet them at work ...'

'So how's Ruth?
Have you seen her?
She looks ten years older.
Is she going to keep the house, do you know?'

'How's the boy?
It will be so hard for him ...
Yes, he's the same age as Luke ...'

I just knew
she was talking about Mark Paine,
and his Mum and his Dad.

Then I saw him.
That night,
when Lizzy and I got to the cinema.

There were loads of people, outside,
waiting to go in.
We were standing in the crowd.

Mark Paine came walking along.
He was pushing at everyone,
trying to get past.
When he saw me,
he stopped.

He just stood there,
looking down at me.

I moved off the pavement,
into the road.

Mark just walked past.
He didn't say anything.
He didn't look back.

Lizzy went mad.

'Did you see that?' she said.
'What did you do that for?'

'What's the problem?' I said.

'Don't let that creep push you around,'
she said.
'He thinks he's so big and strong.'

'If he did that to me,' she went on.
'I'd smack him one.'

I didn't say anything.

I didn't need to fight Mark Paine.
The way I saw it,
I was the strong one.

My family life was OK.
My school work was OK.
I had a job to go to when I left school.

And I had Lizzy.

All the things Mark Paine didn't have.

When I think about it,
Mark always put me down
when girls were there.

It was to make him look big,
and to make me look small.

I didn't mind.

Lizzy said I had to fight Mark Paine
but I wasn't going to fight him.
I just felt sorry for him.

I'd never say that to his face.

If you have enjoyed reading about the Pride Street Crew, you may be interested in other books in the series.

It's Not The Winning
Carrot Rap
You Can't Be A Kid For Ever
She Likes Me
No Turning Back
Child's Play
Damp Dog
Who Do You Love?
Let's Go Shopping
A Thousand Reasons
Make A Splash!
Now I Know How It Feels
You're Never Alone With A Phone